This book is dedicated to all the beautifully diverse families around the world.

And to my beautiful husband, James and children, Jayde,
James Jnr. and Jye (RIP)
You are the reason for my happiness,
I love my little family.
Xox

A special thankyou to Alina who illustrated this book so beautifully, bringing my ideas to life and pouring her heart and soul into it while suffering from the unimaginable; she is from Mariupol Ukraine.

Heritage Prints Publishing

Author: Samantha Trinidad
Illustrator: Alina Shabelnyk
Editor: Rebecca Michael

ISBN: 978-0-6455427-0-7 (Hardback)
ISBN: 978-0-6455427-1-4 (Paperback)
ISBN: 978-0-6455427-2-1 (E-book)

Family is...

Author: Samantha Trinidad

Illustrator: Alina Shabelnyk

Family is. . .

. . .mornings with my daddy and mummy

...bike riding with just my dad

...bedtimes with just my mum

. . .walks in the park with
my two mummies

...beach days with
my dad and step mum

...gardening with
my mum and step dad

...story times with
my foster mum and dad

...football games with
my guardian

...sharing yarns with my grandfather and grandmother

. . .movie nights with
my uncle and aunty

...dancing with
my big sister

...fishing trips with
my big brother

...weekends with
my siblings

. . .art project with my stepbrothers and stepsisters

...camping trips with
my adoptive siblings

...hide-and-seek games
with my cousins

...FaceTime with
relatives who are overseas

...outdoor BBQs together

I love my special family
because. . .

...it is mine!

Draw your family.

Lightning Source UK Ltd.
Milton Keynes UK
UKHW050734310123
416215UK00004BA/56